Recorder *from the* Beginning

C000061798

John Pitts

Pops & Shows helps to increase the range of musical styles available to provide enjoyment for recorder players. The selection features some well-known tunes from the 'pop' field, both old and new, as well as highlights from Disney films and West End and Broadway showstoppers. Also included are some pop-folk items plus three exciting new pieces by John Pitts in rock, blues and boogie styles.

All the items are carefully arranged and graded so that the choice of key and systematic increase in the range of notes (pitches) will make the pieces accessible to as many players as possible. It is expected that players will have already reached the beginning of *Recorder from the Beginning Book 2*, in the author's widely popular teaching scheme. However, the desire to perform a particular piece will provide an incentive to learn any new note or rhythm involved, and personal choice and enjoyment are more likely to dictate the order of pieces played, rather than the order of new notes.

The Pupil's Book includes guitar chord symbols, and the Teacher's Book provides piano accompaniments for all the pieces.

In keeping with the 'repertoire' nature of the book, only a minimum of help or explanation is given. Where more help is required it is best to refer to the appropriate pages of the teaching scheme, *Recorder from the Beginning*.

Chester Music Limited
part of The Music Sales Group
14/15 Berners Street, London, W1T 3LJ, UK

Contents

Notes listed as included do not necessarily appear often in a piece. Some may occur only once or twice! It is best to assess each item individually.

Heartbeat

Words & Music by Bob Montgomery & Norman Petty
Arr. by John Pitts

4

(Piano)

5

On My Own

from *Les Misérables*

Music by Claude-Michel Schonberg, words by Herbert Kretzmer
Original Text by Alain Boublil & Jean-Marc Natel
Arr. by John Pitts

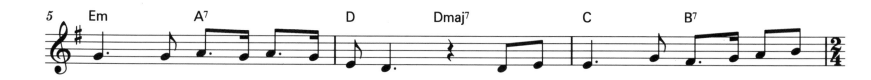

Can You Feel The Love Tonight
from Walt Disney Pictures' *The Lion King*

Music by Elton John, words by Tim Rice
Arr. by John Pitts

9

Another Day In Paradise

Words & Music by Phil Collins
Arr. by John Pitts

11

Yellow Submarine

Words & Music by John Lennon and Paul McCartney
Arr. by John Pitts

1. In the town_____ where I was born lived a man_____ who sailed to

sea. 2. And he told_____ us of his life in the land_____ of sub - ma -

-rines. We all live in a yel - low sub - ma - rine, yel - low sub - ma - rine,

yel - low sub - ma -rine. We all live in a yel - low sub - ma - rine,

yel - low sub - ma - rine, yel - low sub - ma - rine. 3. And our friends_____ are all a -
4. As we live_____ a life of

-board; ma - ny more of them_____ live next door; And the band_____ be - gins to
ease, ev' - ry one of us has all we need. Sky of blue_____ and sea of

play.   (Piano)

green,   in   our   yel – low   sub – ma – rine.

Morning Has Broken

Traditional
Arr. by John Pitts

Not too fast

Scarborough Fair

Traditional
Arr. by John Pitts

14

The Floral Dance

Traditional
Arr. by John Pitts

15

Don't Cry For Me Argentina

from *Evita*

Music by Andrew Lloyd Webber, lyrics by Tim Rice
Arr. by John Pitts

Minty's Moody Blues

John Pitts

18

Sloop John 'B'

Traditional arr. by John Pitts

(Everything I Do) I Do It For You

Words by Bryan Adams & Robert John 'Mutt' Lange
Music by Michael Kamen
Arr. by John Pitts

1. Look in-to my eyes___ you will see___ what you mean to___ me. Search your heart,___ search your soul,___ and when you find me there you'll search_ no more. Don't tell me it's not worth try – in' for, you can't tell me it's not worth dy – in' for. You know it's true___ ev – ery – thing I do, I do it for___ you.

21

Haley's Rock

John Pitts

(Piano)

Beauty And The Beast

from Walt Disney Pictures' *Beauty And The Beast*

Words by Howard Ashman, music by Alan Menken
Arr. by John Pitts

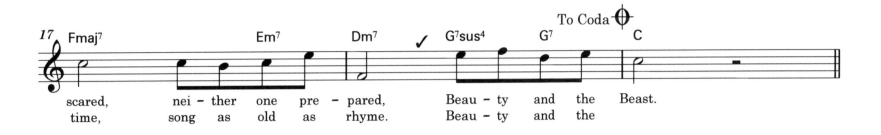

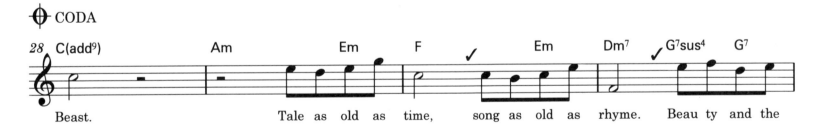

O Sole Mio

Music by Edorado di Capua, words by Giovanni Capurro
Arr. by John Pitts

House Of The Rising Sun

Traditional arr. by John Pitts

Peacherine Rag

Scott Joplin arr. John Pitts

29

Boogie Rock

John Pitts

Brown Girl In The Ring

West Indian Traditional

Fingering Chart
English (Baroque) Fingered Recorders

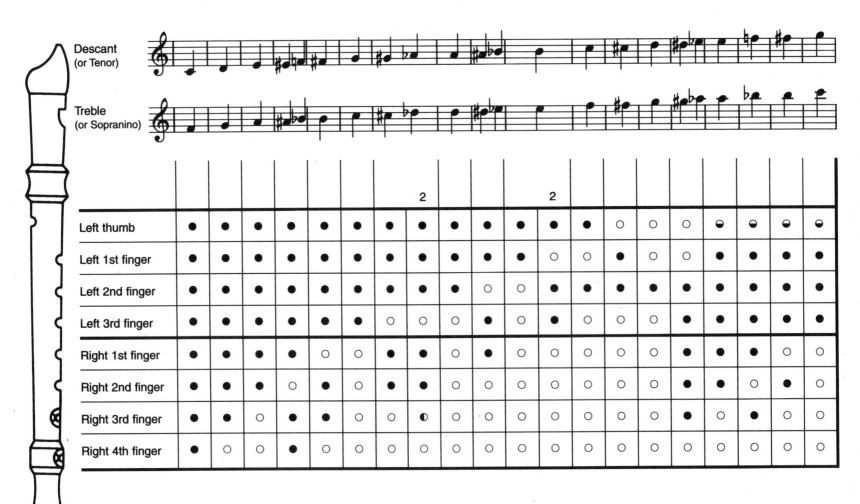

○ Open hole

● Closed hole

◓ Partly closed hole

2 Alternative fingering

12/09 (172290)